SPOT
THE
DIFFERENCE

This edition published in 2007 by Arcturus Publishing Limited
26/27 Bickels Yard, 151–153 Bermondsey Street,
London SE1 3HA

In Canada published for Indigo Books
468 King St W,
Suite 500,
Toronto,
Ontario M5V 1L8

ISBN: 978-1-84193-774-8

Printed in China

Design, Illustration & Copy by quadrum■

SPOT THE DIFFERENCE

Capella

How annoying! The squirrel wants our food.
While we chase him away, can you find eight
differences between these pictures?

Just like these big fish are different from the little fish,
these two pictures are different from each other.
Can you spot 6 differences?

I really enjoy riding my horse. See if you can find the
8 differences between these two pictures
of us before we go for a ride.

Balancing on a wire is very difficult. Especially if you are riding a bicycle with a monkey behind you! But finding 8 differences between these pictures is not difficult, is it?

Look at these friendly giraffes!
Can you spot 9 differences between the two pictures?

The diver has delved into the sea to find 5 differences
between these two pictures. Can you help him?

Snails are really slow creatures. You'll have plenty of time to spot the 5 differences between these pictures, won't you?

The farm girl has run off with the chick and the hen is chasing her. Will the hen catch her before you find 8 differences?

These dinosaurs are waiting for their eggs to hatch. Can you spot 6 differences before the babies arrive?

There are 8 differences between these two pictures of Frank
The Fire-eater and his pet bird. Can you spot them all?

I'm a jolly old centipede and I'm off for a picnic.
But before I go I have to find 5 differences between
these two pictures. Shall we do it together?

It's lunchtime at the farm. Can you look for the 8 differences in the pictures while the pigs enjoy their food?

Trick or treat? This is a tricky game. There are
9 differences in these pictures. Can you find them?

Storks are so lucky! They get to catch their dinner and eat it without having to wait for it to be cooked. Can you spot the 7 differences between these two pictures?

Look at the fun we're having playing in the sea!
Can you spot the 7 differences between the two pictures?

Look at the pictures of Mother Hen and her chicks.
Can you find the 7 differences between them?

Are you wondering why the Space Boys are looking worried?
They can't find the 7 differences between these two pictures.
Will you help them?

We've had great fun playing in the snow. Before we go, can you find 7 differences between these two pictures?

It won't help if you look in the ocean for the 7 differences between these pictures. They are here on these pages!

Farmer Robin is feeding the goose. While he's doing that, can you find 7 differences between these two pictures?

There are 8 differences between these two pictures
of the lion and lioness. Can you spot them all?

There must be something very interesting in the newspaper, everyone's trying to read it! While they are, can you find 8 differences between the two pictures?

46

Wow! Look at the stingray. Isn't it a strange fish?
Can you find 5 differences between the two pictures?

Huff and puff, jogging is so tough. I don't have the energy to spot 7 differences between these pictures. Do you?

Even the three wise men who visited baby Jesus could not find the 8 differences between these two pictures. Can you?

53

Sophie loves Benji. Benji loves his bone. They love to have
fun together. Why don't you have some fun finding
7 differences between these two pictures?

The boys love their balloons. Before they float off, can you spot 7 differences between the two pictures?

We clowns can be funny and do lots of tricks, but we can't find the 8 differences between these two pictures. Can you?

Just like aliens are different from humans, these pictures are different from each other. Can you find 8 differences?

Do you want to go for a ride on the steam train? To get it moving all you have to do is find the 8 differences between the pictures.

Some monsters love flowers just like humans do.
If you can find 6 differences between these two
pictures I will give you these flowers!

Splish-splash, look at all this rain! Can you spot 7 things that are different in the pictures before the rain stops?

What a foolish monkey! He's looking through a telescope to find the 8 differences in these pictures.
You will have to help him.

Look at the ducks swimming in the pond.
Can you spot the 6 differences between the two pictures?

Percy and Chicken are busy looking for 6 differences between these two pictures. Can you help them?

73

The Superplane's pilot is waiting for you to tell him where you'd like him to fly. Maybe you can spot the 6 differences while you make up your mind.

I'm a monster pirate. I can find hidden monster treasure
but I can't find the 6 differences between
these two pictures. Can you help me?

The bear has stolen my honey! He said he would give it back if
I can spot 7 differences between these two pictures.
Please help me find them.

Whee! Look them go! But John and the Birdie look a little unhappy. Let's make them feel better by spotting the 7 things that are different in the two pictures.

80

Come with us on our trip to the zoo. On the way we can spot 6 differences between these two pictures together.

Spot the 6 differences in the picture before
Doggie and Luke whizz past!

85

This lizard here is playing a little picture game. If you look really closely you'll see 5 things that aren't the same.

Watch me splash on the water ring! Can you find the
6 differences between the pictures while you wait your turn?

Look at Peter and his friends having fun at the party!
Can you spot 8 differences between the two pictures?

This lady's getting groceries for dinner. Will you spot the 7 differences between the two pictures while she makes sure she has everything she needs?

These two pictures of people having fun at the beach
look the same don't they? But they are not.
Can you find the 7 differences?

The alien has changed one of these pictures with his powers.
While I defeat him, can you find 8 differences?

We're having loads of fun chasing butterflies.
Come join us and see if you can find 6 things that are
different between the two pictures.

I'm Gooma the Monster. While I perform my fire dance, can you find the 6 differences between these pictures?

It's Uncle John's nap time. Maybe you can help Birdie find
7 differences while he's fast asleep.

Can a lion and a mouse be friends? Yes they can, but only if you find 8 differences between these two pictures!

Boo Boo wants to take you on a boat ride. Just don't forget to spot the 7 differences between the two pictures on the way!

While we sail on the boat and explore,
can you find 8 differences between these pictures?

My name is Lypzeg and I have a twin brother Zeglyp.
One picture is of me and the other is of my brother.
Can you find 6 differences between our pictures?

These pictures of the birds at the zoo look the same,
but if you look carefully you will find 7 differences.

Are these pictures the same? No they are not.
There are 6 differences that we want you to spot!

There are lots of fish in this underwater scene.
There are also 5 differences. Can you find them all?

SOLUTIONS

Page 4

Page 6

Page 8

Page 10

Page 12

Page 14

Page 16

Page 18

Page 20

Page 22

Page 24

Page 26

Page 28

Page 30

Page 32

Page 34

Page 36

Page 38

Page 40

Page 42

Page 44

Page 46

Page 48

Page 50

Page 52

Page 54

Page 56

Page 58

Page 60

Page 62

Page 64

Page 66

Page 68

Page 70

Page 72

Page 74

Page 76

Page 78

Page 80

Page 82

Page 84

Page 86

Page 88

Page 90

Page 92

Page 94

Page 96

Page 98

Page 100

Page 102

Page 104

Page 106

Page 108

Page 110

Page 112

Page 114

Page 116